How To Handle Your
Friends

Scholastic Children's Books,
Commonwealth House, 1–19 New Oxford Street,
London WC1A 1NU, UK
a division of Scholastic Ltd
London ~ New York ~ Toronto ~ Sydney ~ Auckland
Mexico City ~ New Delhi ~ Hong Kong

This edition produced for the Book People Ltd,
Hall Wood Avenue, Haydock, St Helens WA11 9UL

First published in the UK by Scholastic Ltd, 2000

Text copyright © Roy Apps, 2000
Illustrations copyright © Nick Sharratt, 2000

ISBN 0 439 95039 2

How To Handle Your Friends

By Roy Apps

Illustrated by Nick Sharratt

Contents

The clock struck midnight...

Storm clouds blotted out the moon. I heard a noise outside and strolled over to the French doors. Great drops of rain, as big as a man's fist, beat against the windows.

It was a familiar scene. I felt, deep down, as if I had been here before. Then I realized that I had: on page 6 of *How To Handle Your Enemies.**

I shut my eyes. I knew from bitter experience – i.e. from what had happened at the beginning of *How To Handle Your Enemies*, that if I looked out of the window now, I'd see a tall horseman known as Sir Prancelot, dressed in a black suit of armour, burping at me. In other words:

A DARK AND WINDY KNIGHT

*If you want to read *How To Handle Your Enemies*, you can simply buy it in all good bookshops. Or you can even more simply turn this book over.

This was the last thing I wanted. I knew I'd be hauled up on to a horse and whisked off through the rain to go and rescue a damsel in distress. And that horse was the most terrifying creature I'd ever set eyes on. Thinking about it still kept me awake in the small hours. Hardly surprising really, seeing as Sir Prancelot's horse was a *knight mare*.

Quickly, I drew the curtains.

OK, so they didn't look much like a pair of curtains, but have you ever tried drawing with your eyes shut? I opened my eyes and pulled the curtains to.

Then I went to bed.

And so, the very next day...

I was woken up at first light by the sound of someone hammering furiously on my front door. This could mean only one thing: my door bell had broken again.

I rushed downstairs and flung open the front door. There was only one person I knew who pounded the mean streets of our town before all decent people were up, hammering on their doors. And there he stood. Trevor the Milkman.

"One pint of milk and a broccoli and prune flavoured yoghurt, please," I said.

"All in good time," replied Trevor. "First of all I must tell you that I come with a message from a damsel in distress."

"That was Sir Prancelot, the dark and windy knight's line!" I said.*

"He let me have it," explained Trevor the Milkman, "because he didn't need it any more."

"And who is the damsel this time?" I asked.

"Dawn," said Trevor. "Her mum said she

*If you want to check, see *How To Handle Your Enemies*, page 6.

should come and see you herself, but I said I'd tell you. Well, I'm always up before Dawn."

"I don't know … I don't want to go around rescuing damsels in distress," I said.

"Haven't you got the bottle?" asked Trevor.

"No," I replied. "You have. And you've got my broccoli and prune yoghurt."

"Come on!" called Trevor. "We've got to get to Dawn!"

"Not on your Nelly!" I retorted.

"No, not on my Nelly, on my milk float!" said Trevor.

Well, to get back to the pint of the story, Trevor left me my milk and yoghurt and I clambered up on to the back of his milk float.

We set off at top speed. Three hours later we arrived half a kilometre away outside Grunge Hall School.

You may know about the dreadful goings on at Grunge Hall School. If you don't, your name is probably Mr Gibbering-Wreck, Grunge Hall's head teacher.

I saw Dawn wandering up the school drive.

"Dawn!" I called. "My name is Souperman and I have come to rescue you!"

"You're not Souperman," said Dawn. "You're a weedy-looking geek in glasses."

"You wait till I change!" I told her.

I found a phone box and quick as a flash I'd turned myself into Souperman.

"So now you're a weedy-looking geek in a tomato-soup-stained, body-hugging tunic with shoulder pads and red tights?" commented Dawn.

"Huh!" I replied with a pout.

"Oh dear," frowned Dawn. "I hope you haven't taken offence."

"No, I've never taken a fence," I retorted. "That would be stealing."

Dawn shook her head. "My friend Lois said you could help me. You helped her handle Public Enemy Number One."

"You're a friend of Lois's?"

"I *was*," said Dawn. "That's the problem. She's a good mate really, but she tells such dreadful jokes."

"What, like 'What goes up and down and wobbles?'"

"I don't know," said Dawn. "What goes up and down and wobbles?"

"A jellicopter," I answered.

"That's *just* the sort of dreadful joke Lois would tell," sighed Dawn. "The other thing about Lois is, she's just so embarrassing."

"You want to follow Souperman's special course on how to handle your friends!" I said.

"Do I?" asked Dawn.

"Definitely," I insisted.

"OK. When can I start?" asked Dawn.

"As soon as you get to the bit that says ...

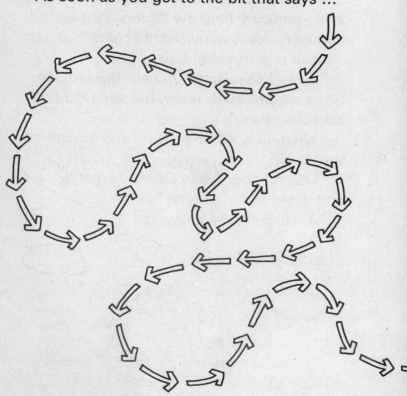

How To Handle Your Friends: Stage One

Friend-type No. 1: **The Corn-y flake-y Friend**

... I replied. "You see, just like enemies and everybody else, the things that friends have *eaten* give them their particular characteristics. Lois is a Corn-y Flake-y Friend. That is, her jokes are corny and some of the things she says and does are just plain flakey."

"Like racing around the playground with her arms outstretched going 'Neee-ahhh!' pretending she's Concorde?" Dawn suggested.

Neee-ahhh!

"That's not being plain flakey," I replied. "That's being *plane* flakey."

"And that pun is really *corny*," muttered Dawn. "So, how do I handle a Corn-y Flake-y Friend like Lois?"

| sat down on the steps and began to tell her.

"What you have to do, Dawn, is … aarghhhhhhhhh!!!!!!!!!!!!"

Unfortunately, the steps I'd sat on belonged to the caretaker and he'd decided he needed them to go and rescue Mr Gibbering-Wreck, the head teacher, who was threatening to jump out of an upstairs window.

"Oh bother," I said. "Look, I've got a enormous ladder in my tights."

"Don't shout about it," said Dawn. "Otherwise the caretaker will want to borrow it to climb up to the window. Anyway, you were going to tell me how to handle a Corn-y Flake-y Friend."

"I expect, like most people with a Corn-y Flake-y Friend, when Lois tells you one of her jokes, you feel like you want to throttle her, don't you?" I asked Dawn.

Dawn nodded.

"You can't really do that," I explained. "Because it would be rather like your mum's description of Sainsbury's on a Friday night, i.e. absolute murder. So, instead of throttling the joker, you should throttle the joke."

I took a couple of things from my cape.
"What are those?" asked Dawn.
"This is my lemonade ..." I explained.

"... and this, over the page, is my visual aid..."

Souperman's Choke-a-Joke Technique

Corn-y Flake-y friends only know corny jokes. And corny jokes always begin "Knock, knock..." Souperman's choke-a-joke technique is a surefire way of making sure your corn-y flake-y friends give up trying to tell you terrible jokes.

door

CFF*: I've got a really good joke! Knock Knock**

YOU: Sounds like someone's at the door.
   You leap up and race to the front door.

*CFF – short for Corn-y Flake-y Friend. It's also short for Crabby old Fish Face which is an extremely rude thing to call a friend, but a very polite thing to call a certain type of crustacean.
**The WORST KNOCK KNOCK JOKE is "Knock knock." "Who's there?" "Arthur." "Arthur Who?" "Arthur mo', I'll open the door and see."

Does your CFF follow you?

Yes	No
YOU: Hi Ian! Yeh, I'll give them to Dad.	YOU: Hi Mrs Barkingmad. Right, I'll tell Mum.
CFF: But there was no one there!	YOU REJOIN YOUR CFF.
YOU: There was. Ian. Ian Visible-Man. Our next door neighbour. He brought Dad a car manual round.	YOU: That was Mrs Barkingmad. Come to tell my mum not to bother to go to the Dog Training Class tonight.
CFF: I can't see any car manual.	CFF: You haven't got a dog!
YOU: That's because it's an invisible man-ual.	YOU: That's why she's not to bother to go to the Dog Training Class.

RESULT: CFF is so baffled by your logic they forget the joke they were going to tell you.

As for handling the flake-y side of CFFs, that's easy-peasy, as I explained to Dawn.

"All you need to do is to make use of the next page of this book!" I said.

"What book's that?" asked Dawn.

"This book's that!" I told her. Then I realized. I hadn't written this book yet! So I did.

Dawn turned the page over. And read...

Souperman's All-Purpose Identikit Face

All you have to do is to choose the nose, ears, eyes and mouth that most closely resemble yours, then stick them on the back of your head.

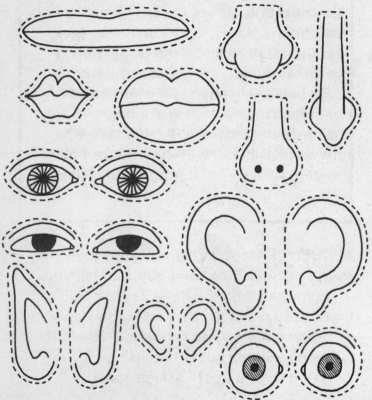

"What's the point of all that?" asked Dawn.

The next time Lois was at Dawn's front door, doing her Concorde impression, I was able to tell her.

"Have you got the Identikit nose, ears, eyes and mouth stuck to the back of your head?" I asked.

Dawn nodded.

"Good! Now simply put your clothes on back-to-front!"

"Souperman, this is stupid!" Dawn protested.

"Stop talking out of the back of your head," I replied.

Dawn put her clothes on back to front.

When she walked off down the road with Lois – who was *still* doing her Concorde impersonations – she didn't look as if she was *with* Lois, but as if she was walking *away* from her!

Neee-ahhh!

Dawn went off with Lois to the school shop, where she bought herself a Strawberry Supawhizziwhirla ice lolly. Unfortunately, she forgot she was dressed back-to-front and tried to eat her Strawberry Supawhizziwhirla through the back of her head.

"Oooo!" she screamed as the ice-cold lolly touched her neck.

Unfortunately, the shock caused her to let go of the lolly and it slipped all the way down her back. After Dawn had run off trying to get her Strawberry Supawhizziwhirla back from inside the front of her T-shirt – not to mention her back back from inside the front of her T-shirt – I sat down with Lois.

"Dawn's a really good mate," sighed Lois, "but she can be a real pain sometimes. She's always up with the very latest fashions, games, bands, in-words and stuff. I can't keep up. It's so exhausting! I wish I knew how to handle her."

Friend-type No. 2: **The Cucumber Friend**

"It sounds to me," I replied, "as if you've got yourself a Cucumber Friend. A cucumber friend is someone who's always trying to be c-o-o-l as a cucumber."

Dawn was on her way to the girls' toilets, jumping up and down and shivering as drips of icy Strawberry Supawhizziwhirla dribbled from her T-shirt.

"Cool?" said Lois. "I should think she's positively *freezing*."

CUCUMBER   CUCUMBER FRIEND

"All you need to be able to handle a Cucumber Friend," I said, "is 'Souperman's Personal Signed Picture of the Coolest Band Ever.'"

Souperman's Personal Signed Picture of the Coolest Band Ever

Next time we saw Dawn, Lois produced her signed picture of B.O. Zone. Dawn immediately became interested.

"Careful," said Lois. "This is my signed picture of B.O. Zone."

"Who?" asked Dawn.

"B.O. Zone! They are BIG! You mean you haven't heard of them?"

"Er ... course I have..." lied Dawn. "Cool."

"Well, they're not so much *cool*, as *hot*," explained Lois. "Especially under the armpits. That's why they're called B.O. Zone. Would you like to borrow my picture of them to put under your pillow?"

"Eurgh... No thanks!" said Dawn.

"Are you sure?" asked Lois. "You could go to sleep with your head in Gary Grunt's armpit."

"I'm through with boy bands. In fact, I'm through with head bands, rubber bands and any other sort of bands for that matter!"

"Cool!" said Lois.

After Dawn had gone, Lois said, "I'm sure I won't have any more trouble with Dawn going on about music, but what about fashion? I could never afford to keep up with the kind of stuff she wears."

"Try these latest styles from the Souperman Fave Fashions Bargain catalogue," I suggested.

Souperman's Fave Fashions

KELVIN KLONE SHADES

UNDERWATER WATCH

STRING VEST

OFFICIAL ENGLAND FOOTBALL TEAM SOCKS – ALWAYS FALLING DOWN; JUST LIKE ENGLAND PLAYERS IN THE GOALMOUTH

JEAN PAUL GROTTIER SHORTS

HIP-HOP SHOES – WITH *INSIDE* SPIKES TO REALLY MAKE YOU HOP!

Lois was desperate to go to some place where no one would recognize her. So would you be if you were dressed up in Kelvin Klone shades, underwater watch, cool vest, Jean Paul Grottier shorts, England football socks and hip-hop shoes.

We ended up in the office of *The Weekly Grunge*, the school newspaper of which Lois was the Agony Aunt.

"I think I can safely say we're alone," said Lois with a sigh of relief.

"I think I can safely say you're a *lune*," piped up a small voice from the corner of the room. "What are you wearing that clobber for?"

"It's the latest designer gear," Lois explained. "At least that's what Souperman says."

"Then whoever designed it should be given the sack," opined the small voice.

"He was. The sack was what he made the vest out of," Lois said. "Anyway, what are you doing in *The Weekly Grunge* office?"

"It's my best friend, Terry Ball-News. I mean he's a good mate, but he's always getting things wrong. It's like my gran's patchwork quilt."

"How do you mean, like your gran's patchwork quilt?" I asked.

"I mean it's *sew* embarrassing," explained the small voice. He turned to Lois. "Can you help me? You are an Agony Aunt."

"*Help* you? After you've been so rude about my designer clothes?" replied Lois crossly. "You must be joking!"

"That's right," smiled the face belonging to the small voice. "I'm Joe King, Nosmo King's little brother."

"You've got a right cheek," snorted Lois.

"I've got a left cheek, too, on the other side of my nose," smiled Joe King. "I suppose I've got another left cheek as well if you count the one..."

"That's enough!" said Lois. "If you think I'm going to help someone who comes into my office without being asked *and* is rude about my clothes, you've got another think coming!"

"Wow!" exclaimed Joe King, excitedly. "You're brilliant! You know everything! I *have* got another think coming! In fact, it's just coming into my brain now and the other think is..." Joe King turned to face me. "The other think is, can *you* help me, Souperman?"

"I can," I said. "Because the way you've described your friend Terry Ball-News, suggests to me that he is the type of friend we call a Rhubarb Fool."

Friend-type No. 3: **The Rhubarb Fool**

"That sounds spot on," nodded Joe King. "Because most of what he says is absolute rhubarb, which makes him sound a right fool. The thing is, what's the best way of handling him?"

"What are the most rhubarb foolish things he says?" I asked.

"I wouldn't dare repeat them," said Joe King, aghast. "Not in public. You'll have to ask him yourself."

We found Joe's mate Terry Ball-News standing in the playground. On his head.

"I'm trying to get the blood to go to my head," said Terry, brightly. And I mean brightly: his face was the colour of a post box. "So that my brain will work better next lesson for our spelling test."

Joe shook his head – Terry's head, that is. Just to make sure it was still connected to his neck.

"Terry," began Joe, "tell me and Souperman what you said the other day about football."

"Just a minute, Joe," said Terry. "After all that standing on my head, my hair's sticking up."

He took his Automatic-Pump-Action-Mega-Water-Pistol and pointed it at his hair. In two seconds flat, his hair was just that. Flat.

"Terry," began Joe, "tell us what you said about football..."

"Do you mean about watching Man U being as exciting as watching a geriatric snail taking his Sunday afternoon walk?"

I was flabbergasted!

"Now Terry," Joe went on, giving me a knowing wink. "What's your opinion of the current music scene?"

"S Crud 6½ are useless," he said. "Even Squidgy Bogies are better than them."

I was flabbergasted. Again.

"I suppose you want to know what I think about films," continued Terry. "Well, for a start *Star Wars* was a load of old tish-tosh."

I was flabbergasted. Again. In fact, never had my flabber been more gasted.

"What do you think, Souperman?" asked Joe. "Can you help me handle Terry?"

"I'm not sure that I can," I replied. "Not only that, I'm not even sure I should."

Now it was the turn of Joe's flabber to be gasted.

"You see," I explained. "Rhubarb Fool friends have their uses. Watch!"

Or, in the case of people reading this book... Read!

Handling a Rhubarb Fool (with a little help from Dr Stew Pidd)

We were approaching I SCREAMO's ICE-CREAM van. The problem was that there were hordes of people all shouting out their orders.

"Fancy an ice-cream?" I asked Joe.

"Course I do, but how can we possibly get ourselves ice-creams at this rate?" answered Joe, glumly.

"No probs," I smiled. "You are about to find out just how useful a Rhubarb Fool Friend can be. Just ask Terry for his opinions on football."

So Joe did just that.

And Terry said, in a very loud voice:*

> I THINK THAT WATCHING MAN U PLAY IS ABOUT AS EXCITING AS WATCHING A GERIATRIC SNAIL TAKING HIS SUNDAY AFTERNOON WALK!

The yelling, screaming crowd around I SCREAMO's van fell silent. When they got up again they were still silent. They had never heard anyone dare criticize Man U before! The way was clear for Joe to place his order!

*The more embarrassing the things a Rhubarb Fool friend says, the louder they tend to say them. Sometimes, like Terry Ball-News, they're so loud they speak IN CAPITAL LETTERS!

"One ice-cream cornet," said Joe to Mr I Screamo, with a big grin, "and a Strawberry Supawhizziwhirla each for me and Souperman!"

When Terry had finished his cornet, he came up to me and said, "Souperman, can I have a word with you on the side?"

"Of course! Fire away!" I replied, immediately lying down on the ground, "No, I don't mean...!!!!"

Unfortunately, I'd forgotten that Terry was still holding his Automatic-Pump-Action-Mega-Water-Pistol. After I'd wrung myself dry, Terry told me what was worrying him.

"It's my mate, Joe. I'm having problems with him."

"*You're* having problems with *him*?"
Terry nodded.

"Well, since he was having problems with *you*, I suppose it's only fair," I commented. "What exactly is the trouble?"

"He has all these mad, bad and extremely dangerous ideas," explained Terry. "And he always wants me to get involved with them."

"Give me an example," I said. But Terry's attention had been taken by his friend Joe, who was calling him. I hid behind a Rose Bush* and listened in to their conversation.

"Guess what," said Joe. "I've got some cream doughnuts to give to Killer Sharkey**!"

"That's kind of you," said Terry. Well, he was a Rhubarb Fool Friend, remember.

*Rose Bush from Year 6 actually. She noticed me immediately – she always was sharp.
**Killer Sharkey is Public Enemy Number One and as such is like your mum when she needs a Christmas Present i.e. to be treated with kid gloves. You can find out a good deal more – and an awful lot bad deal more – about Killer Sharkey, by reading page 38 of *How To Handle Your Enemies*.

"Killer will be really pleased when we give them to him."

Terry offered Killer a cream doughnut. Killer took one bite, then:

"Aaargh!" he said.

"Run for it!" I shouted.

Joe heard my advice and started running off. Then Terry heard my advice and started running after Joe.

Then *I* heard my advice and *I* started running after Terry.

Then, unfortunately, Killer Sharkey heard my advice and he started running after *me*.

I looked over my shoulder.

"It looks as if Killer's fuming!" I yelled to Joe and Terry.

"He's not fuming, he's *foaming*," said Joe. "That cream in those doughnuts was my dad's shaving cream!"

Then I knew just what we were dealing with here, a Jammie Dodger Friend.

Friend-type No. 4: **The Jammie Dodger**

A Jammie Dodger is the kind of friend who's always got some kind of hare-brained scheme on the go, although compared with a Jammie Dodger, a hare has a remarkably large brain.

HARE'S BRAIN

JAMMIE DODGER'S BRAIN

In fact, compared with a Jammie Dodger a *hair* has a remarkably large brain. The trouble is, a Jammie Dodger always gets away with it. His or her best friend, i.e. *you*, doesn't.

Handling a Jammie Dodger Method One: Making Good Your Escape

The most common way of handling a Jammie Dodger is to make sure that you are not around to take the blame for his or her schemes. In other words, always make good your escape. Now there are, of course, two types of escape:

MAKING GOOD YOUR ESCAPE.

MAKING GOOD YOUR S-CAPE.

Most people who need to escape quickly have decent wheels. Unfortunately, a Ferrari may be out of the question. Many Jammie Dodger-type schemes take place in your classroom* – have you ever tried to fit a Ferrari into your work tray? Anyway, you're

*E.g. your Jammie Dodger friend puts superglue in your teacher's box of tissues.

going to be in a hurry, so, as you haven't got a Ferrari you'll have to make sure you always wear your in-line skates in class.

If you can't afford in-line skates, then glue a couple of old bed-springs to the bottom of your trainers. Making sure, of course, that you remove the old bed from them first. Then you can hop off at the slightest sign of Jammie Dodger trouble.

The other way of handling a Jammie Dodger friend, is to learn how to become even more jammie and dodgy than they are...

Killer Sharkey was still chasing us around the school.

Terry Ball-News and Joe King were way ahead now. I couldn't run as fast as them on account of my tights, which were – well – tight.

Killer Sharkey soon caught up with me. He grabbed my shoulder. " 'Ere, Souperman," he said.

"On the side of my head," I replied. "But don't twist it too hard, please."

"No, I mean, you're an expert at handling friends, aren't you?"

I nodded in agreement. That's the best thing to do when Killer Sharkey is holding you by the shoulder.

"I've got a real problem with my best mate," Killer went on.

"You've got a best mate?" I asked. I'd never thought of Public Enemies Number Ones having friends.

"Yeah, he's over there."

Killer pointed out a boy whose head was just like Gloria Giggler's singing, i.e. very flat.

"His name's Ed Basher."

"I can believe it," I replied. "What's the problem?"

"Look at him," said Killer.

So I did. Ed Basher was coming up the school drive on his bike. He was pedalling with one foot and kicking a football with his other foot. In his left hand he was swinging a tennis racquet and in his right hand he was holding a cricket bat. He had a lap top strapped to the handlebars and was punching the keys with a pencil which he held in his mouth.

"You see," sighed Killer. "He's just so *keen* on everything. Football, cricket, tennis, computers, biking... He hardly has any time these days for bashing eds."

"Shame," I said.

Friend-type No 5: **The Mustard Friend**

It was perfectly clear to me what Ed Basher's problem was. "You've got a Mustard Friend," I told Killer. "He's as keen as mustard on everything. The trouble is that having a Mustard Friend is like being a chicken who's laying 20 a day, i.e. eggs-hausting."

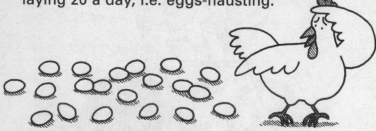

"How do I handle him?" asked Killer.

Handling a Mustard Friend: The low down on the Slow down Method

I used to tell people it was easy peasy to handle a Mustard Friend," I said.

Why don't you tell people it's easy peasy to handle a Mustard Friend now?" asked Killer Sharkey.

"Oh, all right," I said. "It's easy peasy to handle a Mustard Friend. You just need to slow them down. And this is what you need to do to slow him down..."

I gave Killer Sharkey his instructions. Next day, I watched as he carried them out to the letter...

GO TO YOUR
DAD'S BEDROOM.

UNSCREW HIS WEIGHTS
FROM THE BAR.

43

HIRE A MOBILE CRANE.

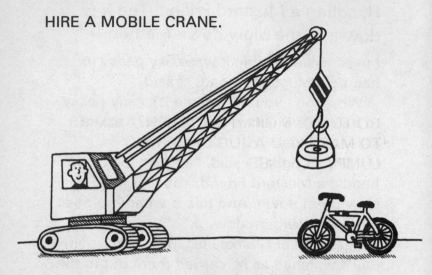

HAVE THE CRANE DROP THE WEIGHTS
OFF BY YOUR FRIEND'S BIKE.

REPLACE BIKE WHEELS WITH THE WEIGHTS.
WHAT A WEIGHT!

GO TO YOUR GRAN'S KITCHEN. ASK HER TO MAKE YOU A JUG OF HER EXTRA LUMPY CUSTARD.

HIRE A MOBILE CRANE.

HAVE THE CRANE DROP THE JUG OF CUSTARD OFF BY YOUR FRIEND'S FOOTBALL.

PUMP THE AMAZINGLY HEAVY EXTRA LUMPY CUSTARD INTO YOUR FRIEND'S FOOTBALL.

WHAT A WEIGHT!

WHAT A WAIT! WHEN YOU HAVE TO HANG ABOUT FOR YOUR MUSTARD FRIEND TO PICK UP THEIR FOOTBALL!

WHAT A WAIT! WHEN YOU HAVE TO HANG ABOUT FOR YOUR MUSTARD FRIEND TO PEDAL OFF ON THEIR BIKE!

RESULT: YOUR MUSTARD FRIEND IS NO LONGER SO KEEN ON FOOTBALL OR BIKING!

I swooped down and patted Killer Sharkey on the back.

"Well done!" I said.

"Thanks Souperman," said Killer. "Swapping Ed's bike wheels for weights and filling his football with custard has really stopped him from being a mustard friend!"

Unfortunately, Ed Basher overheard us.

Now he has a new hobby which he's keen as mustard on: chasing after Killer Sharkey with a big stick, shouting, "I'm gonna do your head in!"

How To Handle Your Friends: Stage Two

The Souperman Friend-Handling Test

1 Eating which of the following kinds of breakfast produces a friend who tells really bad jokes and is embarrassing?

    (i) Toast

    (ii) Muesli

    (iii) Corn flakes

2 Which of the following is useful when handling a Jammie Dodger?

    (i) A Porsche

(ii) A roller

(iii) A jar of jam

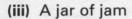

3 In handling Mustard Friends, what are you likely to find is heavier than a lorry load of concrete?

(i) Two lorry loads of concrete.

(ii) Two lorry loads of lorries.

(iii) A jug of your gran's extra lumpy custard.

ANSWERS:

1: (i) Wrong. A friend that eats a lot of toast is the type of friend that keeps popping up from time to time.

(ii) Wrong. A friend that eats a lot of muesli isn't likely to tell bad jokes, but *is* likely to be more than a little nutty.

(iii) Right!!

2: (i) Wrong. A Porsche is only useful for keeping dry in when you're standing on the doorstep.

(ii) Wrong. A roller would certainly be a way of squashing any of your friends' daft dodges. Unfortunately, it would also be a good way of squashing your friend, as well.

(iii) Right!!

3: (i) Right!!

(ii) Right!!!

(iii) Even more right!!!!

HOW TO SCORE:

For each right answer give yourself a tick.
For each wrong answer, give yourself a tock.
For each even more righter answer give
yourself a tick-tock.

2 or more ticks – well done!
You're on your way to
becoming a Souperman.

2 or more tocks – well dumb!
You're on your way to
becoming a Soup –
a Pea-brain Soup, that is.

1 tick-tock – your watch has stopped.

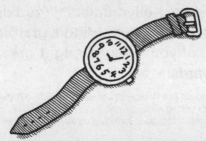

How To Handle Your Friends: Stage Three

The Souperman Guide to Secret Languages for Friends

Sharing a secret language with your friend is a very good way of making sure no one knows what you are talking about.*

One of the most secret languages in the whole world is Gobbablastinian. Never heard of it? That just shows you *how* secret it is. In fact, it's so secret, I haven't heard of it, either.

Because of this, Souperman's recommendation is that you and your friends teach yourselves Diddle. This is a very easy language to learn. In fact, diddle is a doddle.

All you have to do is to say the word "diddle" after every word you speak. So, if you meet one of your friends you might say:

"Hellodiddle, Kellydiddle.** Youdiddle goingdiddle todiddle yourdiddle gran'sdiddle?"

And one of your friends might greet you with the words:

*Though if your friend is a Rhubarb Fool (see pages 28-32) they won't know what they're talking about, either.
**You are, of course, addressing Kelly Ogg, your Corn-y Flake-y Friend.

"Heydiddle! Youdiddle cooldiddle dude-diddle! Funkydiddle daydiddle mandiddle!"*
Now!!!!!!! Practise the following diddle phrases!!!!

> **1** "Diddiddle youdiddle seediddle Eckdiddle anddiddle Duncediddle** ondiddle teediddle veediddle?"

> **2** "Candiddle Ididdle borrowdiddle yourdiddle Garydiddle Gormlessdiddle Ceediddle Deediddle?"

> **3** "Heydiddle diddlediddle diddlediddle, thediddle catdiddle anddiddle thediddle fiddlediddle."

*At least, that's what they'll say if they're a Cucumber Friend.
**Eck and Dunce, the famous laddish TV presenters from Newcastle.

How To Handle Your Friends: Stage Four

The Souperman Very Personal Friend File

1: YOUR BEST CORN-Y FLAKE-Y FRIEND

NAME: ....

MOST EMBARRASSING JOKE: ....

2: YOUR BEST CUCUMBER FRIEND

NAME: ....

COOLEST ITEM OF GEAR: ....

3: YOUR BEST RHUBARB FOOL FRIEND

NAME: ....

TWITTIEST SAYING: ....

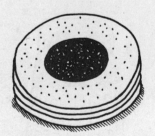

4: YOUR BEST JAMMIE DODGER FRIEND

NAME: ....

MOST DANGEROUS DODGE: ....

5: YOUR BEST MUSTARD FRIEND

NAME: ....

THEIR HOBBIES, PASTIMES, INTERESTS, ACTIVITIES ETC (continue in separate 200-page exercise book if necessary): ....
....
....
....
....
....
....
....
....
....
....
....
....
....

WARNING!!!!
DANGER!!!!

You are now leaving the *How To Handle Your Friends* zone. Beyond this point are 55 pages of Souperman's advice on *How To Handle Your Enemies*. Obviously, some of the details of what enemies get up to is pretty gruesome, while the rest of the details of what enemies get up to is ugly gruesome.

SO BEWARE!!!!

If you suffer badly from nerves, you should put this book down now. If, on the other hand, as opposed to suffering badly from nerves, you suffer badly from *nerds*, you should turn this book round and read *How To Handle Your Enemies* without a second thought. Better still, turn this book round and read *How To Handle Your Enemies* without a *first* thought.

WARNING!!!!
DANGER!!!!

You are now leaving the *How To Handle Your Enemies* zone. Beyond this point are 29 odd pages of Souperman's advice on *How To Handle Your Friends* plus 28 not-so-odd pages of Souperman's advice on *How To Handle Your Friends*.

BEWARE!!!!

However, if your friends discover that you are finding out how to handle them, they might be hurt. Not only that, you might be hurt, i.e. when they hit you over the head with a copy of this book.

Nemi: .....COPPW.....................................

Pabloc Inimy Nambir:......three...........................

Typi uf Pabloc Inimy:......The Big Whoppa.....

Mithud Fur Hendlong Hom/Hir:...out-Smarting

Deti uf Forst Saccissfal Hendlong:.....6/11/R09...

CUNFODINTOEL

Mithud Fur Hendlong Hom/Hir: Jekyll + Hyde

CUNFODINTOEL

Deti uf Forst Saccissfal Hendlong 6/1/2019

Nemi: RO

Pabloc Inimy Nambir: $1\frac{1}{2}$

Typi uf Pabloc Inimy: Bangers + Mash,

Mithud Fur Hendlong Hom/Hir: Imposter

TUP SICRIT

Deti uf Forst Saccissfal Hendlong: 6/1/2019

How To Handle Your Enemies: Stage Four

The Souperman Very Personal Pabloc
Inimy Fole

Nemi: Snew

Pabloc Inimy Nambir: Fuar

Typi uf Pabloc Inimy: Tu Ady in the hole.

Mithud Fur Hendlong Hom/Hir: Make miss twenty hate ner

PROVETI

Deti uf Forst Saccissfal Hendlong: 6/1/2019

Nemi: Rudy

Pabloc Inimy Nambir: One

Typi uf Pabloc Inimy: Ratito

How To Handle Your Enemies

Scholastic Children's Books,
Commonwealth House, 1–19 New Oxford Street,
London WC1A 1NU, UK
a division of Scholastic Ltd
London ~ New York ~ Toronto ~ Sydney ~ Auckland
Mexico City ~ New Delhi ~ Hong Kong

This edition produced for the Book People Ltd,
Hall Wood Avenue, Haydock, St Helens WA11 9UL

First published in the UK by Scholastic Ltd, 2000

ISBN 0 439 95039 2

All rights reserved
Printed and bound by Nørhaven Paperback A/S, Denmark

10 9 8 7 6 5 4 3 2 1

How To Handle Your Enemies

By Roy Apps

Illustrated by Nick Sharratt

Contents

The clock struck midnight...

Storm clouds blotted out the moon. I heard a noise outside and strolled over to the French doors. Great drops of rain, as big as a man's fist, beat against the windows. The wind was moaning. The French doors were moaning.

I looked again and saw that the great drops of rain *were* a man's fist! I opened the French doors. There stood a tall stranger in a black suit of armour. The figure lifted the visor from its face, then burped, loudly. Yes, there was no doubt about it, it was a dark and windy knight.

"Greetings sire," said the knight. "My name is Sir Prancelot and I come with a message from a damsel in distress."

"If she's out in this weather," I replied. "She's more likely to be a *damp*-sel in distress!"

"She goes to Grunge Hall school," Sir Prancelot went on.

"Grunge Hall?" I gasped. "The school that's so tough, the teachers walk about in pairs?"

"The very same, sire," said Sir Prancelot. "Except now, it's not the same. It's even worse. Not only are the teachers walking about in pairs, the children are walking about in apples."

"Their lives are being made a misery by a group of bullies, liars, cheats and sneaks."

"Goodness," I said. "Are they still having trouble with their teachers?"

"No sire, it's not the teachers," replied Sir Prancelot. "Everyone's learnt how to handle the teachers, thanks to your wondrous book,* but they're having real trouble with some top enemy types in their class. I mentioned a damsel in distress…

"Did you?"

"Yes, on page six."

I looked back to page six and found that Sir Prancelot was right.

"The damsel in question is Lois Lune, editor of the Grunge Hall School newspaper *The Weekly Grunge*. She has been swamped with letters for her Agony Aunt column from classmates who are suffering at the hands of top enemy types. She's worried frantic."

"There's no point her worrying Fran Tic about it," I retorted. "Fran knows nothing of such matters. No, I am the man for this job."

"Then, sire," exclaimed Sir Lancelot, "we must make haste!"

I got down my *Blue Peter Big Rainy Day Book* and tried to find a chapter on how to make "Haste" using old yoghurt pots and sticky-backed plastic, but I couldn't.

"I'll give you a lift, sire," cried Sir Prancelot. "Just hop up on to the back of my trusty steed!"

"You're on!" I said. "And so am I!"

"You are *on*, but you're on the wrong way round, sire," said Sir Prancelot.

Off we rode towards Grunge Hall School; Sir Prancelot grasping a sword in his hand and me grasping an umbrella in mine.

"I'm afraid, sire, I'll have to drop you off here," said Sir Prancelot, as we pulled up at some traffic lights.

Sir Prancelot lifted me up and dropped me on to the pavement.

"I've got to get back to school," he said.

"But it's almost bedtime," I exclaimed.

"That's right, sire. Being a knight I go to night school."

"Of course," I replied.

"Good night, sire," said Sir Prancelot.

"Night, knight," said I.

It was important that I find a phone box. I saw one at the end of the street. I ran along the pavement, straight into it.

I picked myself up. Then I put myself down again. I opened the door to the handy phone box and walked in.

There was a good reason I needed a phone box: it was still raining and I didn't want to get wet.

There was another reason I needed a phone box. Teaching Lois Lune and her mates how to handle their enemies was not a task for an ordinary human being. Super human powers were required. I *had* those super human powers. First, though, I had to become a different person. I took off my anorak and glasses. I spun myself round. As I banged my elbows on the phone and my knees on the door, I muttered the familiar refrain:

"Aargh! Ow! Ouch!"

With one bound, I leapt from the phone box and stood on the pavement, hands on my hips. Gone were my embarrassing black-rimmed glasses and anorak. Instead, I was wearing a bright-blue, body-hugging tunic with shoulder pads and a pair of red tights. Cool, or what?

I looked down at the familiar orange  stains on my tunic. Yes, I was Souperman. During my childhood, I had been caught up in a terrific explosion. My dad had been trying to open a can of tomato soup with a hammer. (He'd lost the can opener.) Suddenly, as he hit the can, it exploded and tomato soup shot all over me. From that day, I found I had special powers – Souperman powers.

I climbed up on to the phone box and prepared to fly at the speed of light to Lois Lune's rescue. I stepped off the roof.

"Aaaaaargh..."

I sat up on the pavement and suddenly remembered: my Souperman powers didn't include being able to fly.

So I got the bus to Grunge Hall School instead.

Then as the school wasn't due to open till nine o'clock the next morning, I went across the road to the park and found a bed for the night.

Unfortunately, it was a rose bed, so I didn't sleep too well.

And so, the very next day...

...just before school, I went along to Lois Lune's classroom. There were two girls sitting there, but I didn't know which one was Lois.

"Which one of you is a damsel in distress?" I asked.

"I'm a damsel in this dress, and she's a damsel in that dress," replied one of the girls.

"Then you must be Lois Lune," I said. "Do you know who I am?"

Lois shook her head.

"What do you think the 'S' on my chest stands for?" I said.

Lois frowned at my tomato-soup-stained, bright-blue, body-hugging tunic with shoulder pads. " 'S' for ... Sloppy eater?" she suggested. Then she looked at my red tights. "No," she said, "it must be Soppy eater!"

"No," I replied. "I am here to teach you and your mates how to handle your enemies."

Lois jumped up in excitement. "Then you're just in time!"

"No, I'm not Jess Tintime," I told her. "You're mistaking me for someone else. *I* am Souperman."

Lois led me over to the book corner. She told me to sit down on a bean bag. It was old, ripped and uncomfortable. In fact, it wasn't so much a bean bag as a *has* bean bag.

"First of all, Lois," I said, "let me tell you how enemies are made."

How To Handle Your Enemies: Stage One

How enemies are made

"There are two ways to make an enemy," I began. "The first way is to find the biggest, grottiest boy in your class and jump up and down on his toes. That way you'll have made an enemy for life."

AARGH!

"And two?" enquired Lois.

"Give them something good to eat – or rather *bad* to eat. You see, enemies *are* what they eat, just like the rest of us."

Lois looked hard at me. "I see what you mean," she said. "You obviously eat a lot of cauliflower cheese and peas."

I frowned.

"You've got cauliflower ears, cheesy feet and a pea brain," Lois explained.

"I've also got tomato sauce stains on my tunic, which give me my Souperman powers," I retorted. "In the same way, the things that enemies have eaten give them their particular horrible characteristics. Only when you know exactly what enemy-type you are facing can you possibly begin to learn how to handle them."

Lois looked thoughtful. "Humm," she said.

"*Humm humm, every humm humm needs good neighbours,*" I hummed.

"No!" sighed Lois. "I meant 'hum' why don't I show you all the letters I've had in my position as Agony Aunt on *The Weekly Grunge* from people who can't handle their enemies?"

"I don't know, why don't you show me all the letters you've had from people who can't handle their enemies in your position as Agony Aunt on *The Weekly Grunge*?"

Lois grabbed my arm and dragged me off to a small room at the far end of the school.

The sign on the door said:

THE WEEKLY GRUNGE NEWSPAPER OFFICE

This was the first time in my life that I had been spoken to by a sign on the door.

In one corner of the office was a great mountain of mail. In another corner of the office was a great mountain of male.

"Come here," yelled the mountain of male, "I wanna bash your head in!"

"Run for it!" shouted Lois.

I ran straight at the mountain of male.

"No, I didn't mean run *at* it, I meant run away from it!" yelled Lois.

We tore down the school corridor. Then we tore down the door.

"Don't worry, Mr Grott the caretaker will put it back up," said Lois, breathlessly.

We stood outside the sweetshop opposite the school gates. We were both out of breath. I went into the shop to buy some more, but they were out of breath, too.

We sat down on the pavement.

"That," said Lois, "was Billy Bonegrinder."

"He looked very much like a Public Enemy Number One and a Half – a Bangers and Mash enemy." I said. "Let me explain..."

Public Enemy No. 1½: **The Bangers and Mash Enemy**

"A Bangers and Mash enemy is so called because he or she likes nothing more than a decent head to bang. Unfortunately, the decent head in question is inevitably going to be *yours*. Next to banging your head, the Bangers and Mash enemy's fave pastime is mashing a head. This is also likely to be your head, too. In fact, unless you have *two* heads – e.g. one on your neck and a spare one in your sock drawer – the head of yours that gets the banging will be exactly the same head that gets the mashing."

BANGERS
AND MASH

A HEAD BEING
BANGED

A HEAD BEING
MASHED

"Yes, I see the problem," said Lois.

"So do I!" I replied. "And he's racing out of the school gates on his way over here!"

Off we ran. Then, on we ran. In fact, we ran off and on, mainly because we were still out of breath. We managed to escape from Billy Bonegrinder though, by hiding amongst some school jumpers.

In the playground, Lois asked me, "How exactly do you handle a Bangers and Mash enemy, then?"

"I'm glad you asked me that," I replied.

"Are you?" said Lois.

"Yes," I answered, "because it's the title of the very next bit in this book."

Handling a Bangers and Mash Enemy: The Imposter Method

"So it is," said Lois.

"What you need to handle a Bangers and Mash enemy," I explained, "is an imposter. Unless your Bangers and Mash enemy is a girl, in which case, of course, you need a *her*poster. Someone who can impersonate you." I looked across the playground. "Who is the teacher on break duty?"

"That's Miss Vark," said Lois.

"She looks to me as if she might be one of the hard Varks," I said.

"She is," nodded Lois. "She even keeps mums and dads in if she catches them talking at parents' evenings."

The Set Up:

I strolled up to Miss Vark. "Excuse me, Miss Vark," I said. "Would you mind looking after my tunic, only I've promised to help Mr Grott the caretaker clean his collection of

medieval instruments of torture and it's hot work!"

"Not at all," said Miss Vark and she slipped my tunic round her shoulders.

Presently, Lois and I saw Billy Bonegrinder sneaking up behind Miss Vark.

"I'm gonna bash your head in!" he yelled, mistaking the two-metre tall PE teacher for me.

He leapt on to her back and started pummelling her about the ears.

"Yee-argh!" yelled Miss Vark.

"Yee-argh!" yelled Billy Bonegrinder, when he realized his mistake.

The Result:

The result was that Miss Vark was very cross indeed. In fact, the deed she did next was a very cross deed indeed.

"You will stay in every playtime for the rest of—" she began.

"Not the rest of term!" blubbered Billy Bonegrinder, pathetically.

"No, not for the rest of term!" seethed Miss Vark.

"Oh good," said Billy Bonegrinder, with relief.

"For the rest of *your life!*" roared Miss Vark.

"Wow, Souperman, I'm impressed!" smiled Lois.

She was, too. Unlike Billy Bonegrinder who was not so much *im*pressed as *de*pressed.

Lois frowned. "There's something here that's really peculiar."

"That's what a lot of people say the first time they meet me."

Lois shook her head. "No, I mean, Billy Bonegrinder was the first Public Enemy that we met but you said he was Public Enemy number one *and a half.*"

"That's because the title Public Enemy Number One is reserved for the sneakiest

enemy of all. Compared to Public Enemy Number One, Billy Bonegrinder is a great big softie."

Lois shivered. "This Public Enemy Number One. Is he in my class?"

I shook my head. "He's in a class all of his own. Don't worry," I said. "I'll know him when I see him."

Public Enemy No. 2: **The Chicken Tikka Enemy**

Back in *The Weekly Grunge* office, Lois showed me a letter she had received which was really troubling her.

"It's a very sad letter," she explained.

She was right. This letter looked so sad, there were tears falling from the envelope. I looked more closely at it.

"No wonder it's a sad letter," I cried. "Look at the front of the envelope, it's been stamped on!"

"Aw, painful," winced Lois.

I took the letter from the envelope. This is what I read:

Dear Lois Lune

Everywhere I go I am being plagued by this person – Felicity Foulmouth – who keeps calling me rude and horrible names.

Please can you help me to learn how to handle her? I am desperate.

Yours sincerely
Des Perate

"There's no doubt about it," I said. "Des Perate's tormentor is a Chicken Tikka Enemy, so called because everything they stuff into their mouths is fowl and everything that comes out of their mouths is foul."

"Oh no!" exclaimed Lois, looking towards the door. "Time is running out!"

"Then let's run after it!" I said.

So we did. We didn't manage to catch up with it, but we did manage to catch up with Des Perate. Felicity Foulmouth was standing next to him. She was in full flow:

You're a jelly-welly baby! You're a blabby blubberer! You're spotty, you're snotty, you need a baby's potty!

Des was trying to hide behind the netball post. This was not a cool idea, because his ears stuck out.

Lois told Des who I was.

"WOW ARE YOU REALLY SUPERMAN?"

Then she told him who I wasn't.

"NO, HE'S NOT SUPERMAN, HE'S *SOUPERMAN!*"

All you need to be able to handle a Chicken Tikka Enemy," I said, "is Souperman's Chicken Tikka Enemy Handy Recipe Card."

Souperman's Chicken Tikka Enemy Handy Recipe Card

1: Take something hot – like a CHILLI.

2: Take something chilly – like an ICE LOLLY.

3: Take something tasty – like an ONION.

4: Take something smelly – like GORGONZOLA CHEESE.

5: Mix it all together with a hot CURRY paste.

CURRY PASTE
HOT!!!!

6: Serve into your Chicken Tikka Enemy's lunch box.

The Result:
Des followed the recipe instructions.

He sat down for lunch in the hall. Felicity Foulmouth opened her mouth to shout some rude and horrible things at him. First, though, she took a bite from her chicken tikka sandwich. And, of course, out of her mouth came not a string of rude and horrible names, but..."

"Aargh!"

"Owww!"

"Oooo..."

"Urgh!"

And again, when Felicity Foulmouth opened her mouth the second time what came out wasn't a string of rude and horrible names either, but bits of half-chewed chillies, ice lolly, onions, Gorgonzola cheese and curry paste.

"Aye-e-h! Thanks Lois! Thanks Souperman!" said Des Perate.

At least, that's what I *think* he said. Only he was speaking a bit muffled, owing to the fact that he'd pulled his anorak hood down over his face to protect himself from the bits of half-chewed chillies, ice lolly, onions, Gorgonzola cheese and curry paste spewing from Felicity Foulmouth's mouth.

Public Enemy No 3: **The Big Whoppa Enemy**

"That's super, man!" said Lois.

"No that's Felicity Foulmouth, *I'm* Souperman," I replied.

"Could you help me with some more of my readers' problems?" asked Lois.

"Lead on!" I replied. "No, I didn't mean that sort of 'lead on'."

But too late. Lois had already slipped a collar round my neck and was hauling me back to *The Weekly Grunge* office.

Lois gave me the next letter from her mail bag to read:

Dear Lois,

I need your help.
It's Shane Swagger. He keeps boasting all the time. He's always saying he's better at everything than everyone else. It makes me sick.
Can you tell me how to handle him?

Yours sincerely
Luke Howt

"I know just what this Shane Swagger sounds like," I said.

"Do you?" said Lois. "That's amazing, 'cos you've never even heard him speak!"

"All part of my Soupermanic powers," I replied. "Shane is what we call a Big Whoppa Enemy. In other words, he's always telling big whoppers."

"Back to the playground, then!" commanded Lois.

"If you insist," I replied. "Hey, Luke Howt!" shouted Lois.

Everyone ducked. Except me, that is. Well, it's hard to duck when you're lying flat on the ground.

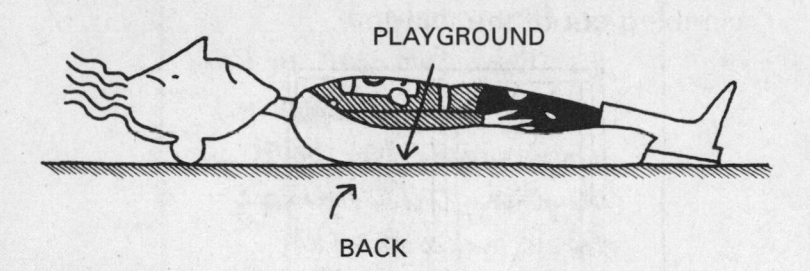

PLAYGROUND

BACK

Handling a Big Whoppa Enemy: The Thin Door/Fat Head Method

"There are two ways of handling a Big Whoppa Enemy," I explained to Luke. "The first way is to make sure you only ever go into rooms that have small openings, i.e. thin doors. That way the Big Whoppa Enemy is bound to get his big fat head stuck in the door."

"There's only *one* problem

with the Thin Door/Fat Head method of
handling a Big Whoppa Enemy," I continued,
"and it's this—"

Suddenly, I was interrupted by a sneering
voice going...

"NER NER NER NER NER!"

We turned round to see Shane Swagger
climbing out of the window.

"If the door's too small for my head, I just
climb through the window. See, I'm brilliant,
I am. I could join MENSA I could, only I'm
too brainy for them."

"Like I said," I said, "there is only one
problem with the Thin Door/Fat Head method
of handling a Big Whoppa Enemy... It
doesn't work."

What's the second way of handling a Big
Whoppa Enemy, then?" asked Luke. He
looked like a sumo wrestler who's just eaten
30 dinners, i.e. totally fed up.

I put my hand inside my tunic and whisked
out a card.

"Just follow the instructions," I said.

Luke read the card. "The Sooty and Co Fan Club Membership Card...?"

"Oops, sorry, wrong card," I replied, quickly swapping it for the right one, which read:

Handling a Big Whoppa Enemy: The Turning Him Into a Little Squirt Method, Option One

1: Put the Big Whoppa into a food blender.

2: Turn on food blender.

3: Tip resulting liquid into a water pistol.

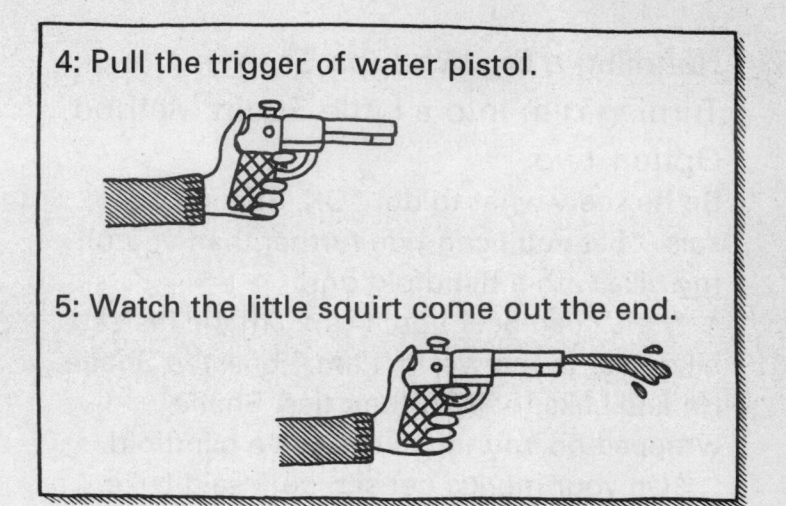

4: Pull the trigger of water pistol.

5: Watch the little squirt come out the end.

Luke was a fast runner. He had no trouble catching Shane Swagger. The only trouble was, he wouldn't fit into the school kitchen's food blender.

Shane was livid. He was furious. He was *mad*. He was a bit cross as well.

"I'll get you, Luke Howt!" he fumed.

Luckily, Luke had read the instructions for:

Handling a Big Whoppa Enemy: The Turning Him Into a Little Squirt Method, Option Two

So he knew what to do. "OK, Shane," he said. "Bet you I can ride further than you on my bike with a blindfold on!"

"Pah. I can beat you, I can. I'm the fastest bike rider in the world, I am," boasted Shane. He and Luke took off their ties. Shane wrapped his round his eyes as a blindfold.

"On your marks, get set, go!" said Luke.

"Aaaaaaargh!!!!!" said Shane, as he immediately crashed into the three-metre-high hawthorn hedge in front of the head teacher's office window.

When Luke ran back in triumph from doing a circuit round the playing field, Shane yelled "You cheated! You didn't have a blindfold on!"

"The bet," said Luke calmly, "was to ride *a bike with a blindfold on*. That's why I put the blindfold on my bike, so it was *a bike with a blindfold on*. Why you had to tie a blindfold round

your eyes, I don't know! What a nitty-twitty
you are!"

Shane Swagger pouted and cringed like
the little squirt he now was. And from that
day on to this day off, he never ever boasted
to Luke Howt again.

Public Enemy No. 4: **The Toady-in-the-Hole Enemy**

After we'd finished pulling the thorns out of
Shane Swagger's hair, Lois and I strolled
back into school. Suddenly, we heard a voice
behind us calling out to a teacher on the far
side of the playground.

"Please Miss, Lois Lune is with a boy and
he's not wearing school uniform!"

Lois groaned. "That's Virginia Creeper,"
she sighed. "She's always sneaking to the
teachers about something or other."

"She's what's known as a Toady-in-the-
Hole Enemy," I said.

"I wish *she* was down a hole," muttered
Lois.

"If you follow Souperman's Easy-Peasy
Plan for handling Toady-in-the-Hole
Enemies," I replied, "Virginia Creeper will
wish she was down a hole."

I gave Lois the instructions on handling

Toady-in-the-Hole enemies, while I sat in the hall writing out 100 times: I MUST NOT WEAR RED TIGHTS TO SCHOOL.

"I hope this plan is Easy-Peasy," she frowned.

"It's a doddle!" I said. "As opposed to the squiggle at the bottom of the Easy-Peasy Plan, which is a *doodle*!"

Souperman's Easy-Peasy Plan for Handling a Toady-in-the-Hole Enemy

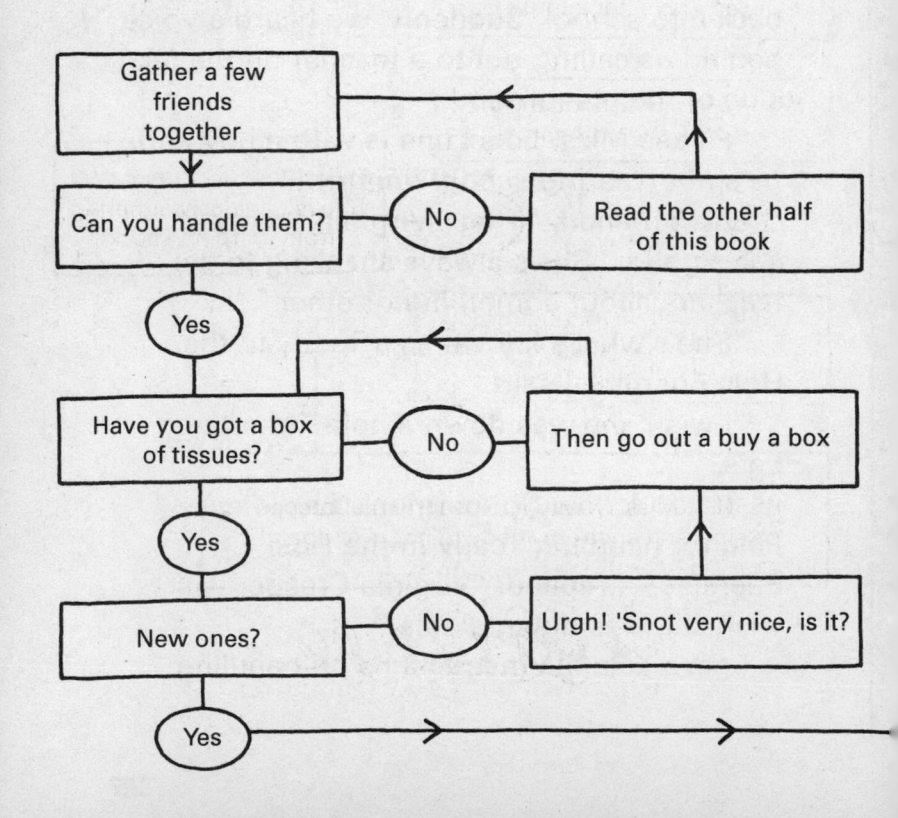

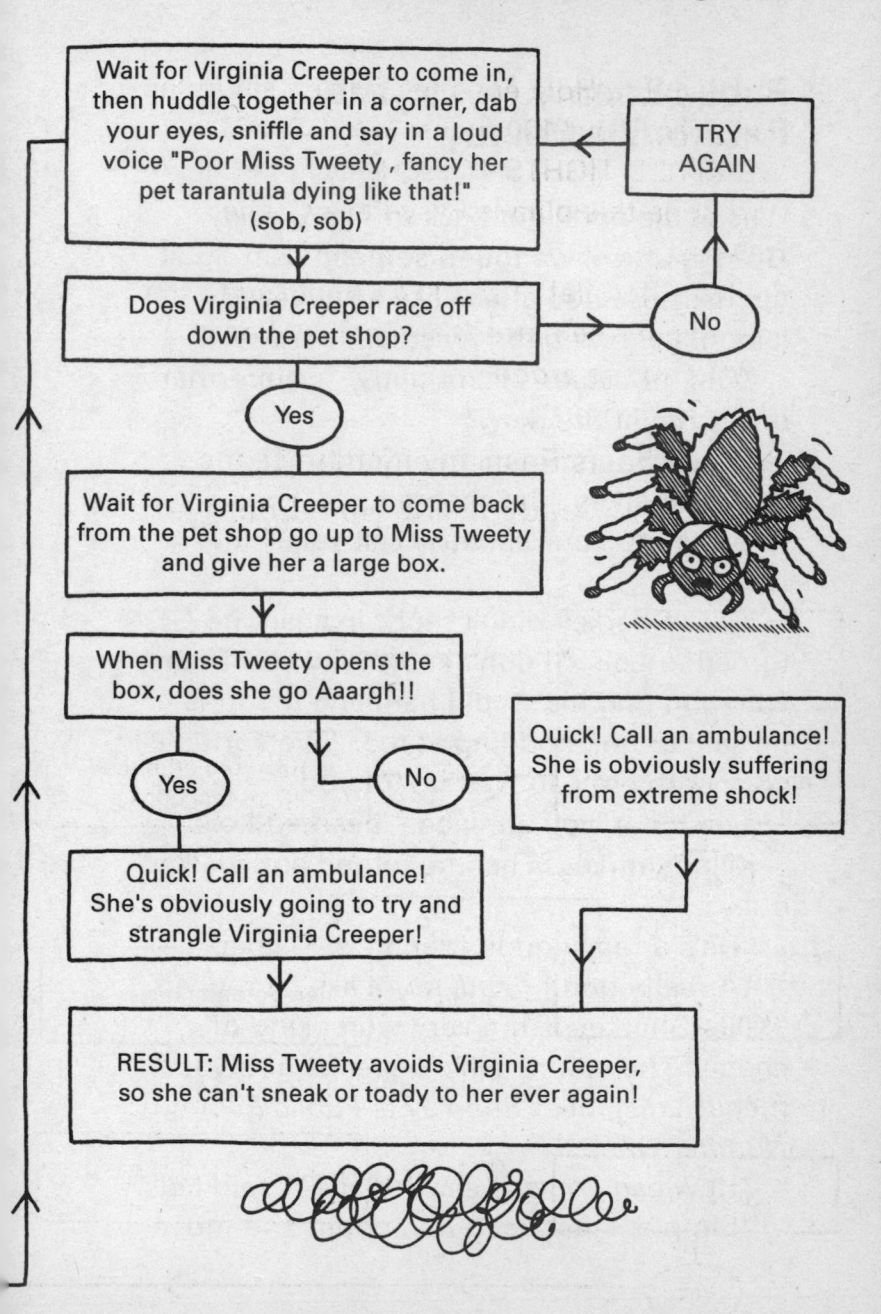

Wait for Virginia Creeper to come in, then huddle together in a corner, dab your eyes, sniffle and say in a loud voice "Poor Miss Tweety , fancy her pet tarantula dying like that!" (sob, sob)

TRY AGAIN

Does Virginia Creeper race off down the pet shop?

No

Yes

Wait for Virginia Creeper to come back from the pet shop go up to Miss Tweety and give her a large box.

When Miss Tweety opens the box, does she go Aaargh!!

No

Yes

Quick! Call an ambulance! She is obviously suffering from extreme shock!

Quick! Call an ambulance! She's obviously going to try and strangle Virginia Creeper!

RESULT: Miss Tweety avoids Virginia Creeper, so she can't sneak or toady to her ever again!

Public Enemy No. 5: **The Ratatouille Enemy**

When Lois and I got back to *The Weekly Grunge* office, we found someone sitting at her desk. He had a face like a squeezed lemon, i.e. bitter and twisted.

"Oh, hi!" said Lois, brightly. "Souperman, this is Kevin Sharkey."

"Hello Souperman, my friends call me 'Killer' Sharkey," he sneered.

"What do your *enemies* call you?" I retorted.

Killer Sharkey didn't reply. Instead, he turned to Lois. "I don't know why you bother with him and his stupid handling theories," he said to her, nodding at me. "I've sorted all your problem page letters for you."

"Oh Killer, you are kind," beamed Lois.

Killer smirked. Then he turned and walked out.

"He's a really good friend," said Lois.

"A really good *fiend*, more like," I replied. "Killer Sharkey is the very worst kind of enemy. The enemy who *pretends* he's your friend! Lois, Killer Sharkey is *Public Enemy Number One*!"

"How can you say such things?" said Lois.

"Simple, I just open my mouth and move

my jaw up and down!" I explained.

"How can you be sure?" frowned Lois.

"Look at the heading on page 38," I replied.

"But Killer's replied to all my problem page letters for me!" protested Lois.

"Open one of his replies and see what he's written," I said.

Lois ripped open an envelope and took out the letter. This is what we read:

Dear Ali Pally

Thank you for your letter about how you really fancy Suzi Woozi and want to take her to the school disco but are too shy and embarrassed to tell her. The solution is simple. Give me £5 and I'll tell her for you. Give me another £5 and I won't pin your letter up on the class noticeboard. What could be more simple than that?

Your mate,
Killer Sharkey

"Sounds like bribery!" exclaimed Lois.

"Library," I said.

"Pardon?" asked Lois.

"Library. That sounds like Bribery," I said.

"There must be some mistake. Killer would never resort to bribery. He's a mate! He's all right!" protested Lois.

"He's all rat," I replied. "Or to be precise, he's a rat who's always getting other people in a stew. In other words, a Ratatouille Enemy."

"I don't believe it!" muttered Lois, despondently.

"We can prove it once and for all," I said, "by using the Jekyll and Hyde method. Dr Jekyll was a doctor who invented a potion that turned him into an evil monster called Mr Hyde. You must do something very similair."

"I've got to turn into an evil monster called Mr Hyde?"

"No, the Hyde bit is what you've got to *do*! Preferably behind a hideous mask. That way Killer won't recognize you. You see, the important thing with Ratatouille Enemies is to know who they are. That way they can do you no harm."

"But where can I get such a mask?" asked Lois.

"On page 41 of a very wonderful book

called *How To Handle Your Enemies*," I replied.

Souperman's Ratatouille-Enemy-Handling Mask*

Once Lois had her mask on, I said, "Right that's the Hyde bit sorted, now for the Dr Jekyll bit."

"Have I got to become Dr Jekyll?" asked Lois.

"Forget the 'Je'," I replied. "Just stick with becoming Dr Kyll. Come on, we're going to the shopping centre."

I explained the plan to her, going into Great Detail. And Lois went with me.

When we came out, we saw Killer Sharkey coming along. Lois went up to him and said "Hi!"

Killer Sharkey frowned at her. "Are you new here?"

Lois nodded. "My name's Glois Glune."

"Why have you got a beard, Glois?"

"Where I come from, all the girls wear beards," said Lois, calmly.

"Where's that?" asked Killer Sharkey.

"Hairyford," answered Lois. "Tell me do you know a girl called Lois Lune?"

(This was the *crucial* bit of the plan. If Killer Sharkey said nice things about Lois, it would show he was a friend. If not it would show he truly was a Ratatouille Enemy.)

"Lois Lune?" repeated Killer. "Eurgh! She does that problem page in *The Weekly Grunge*. It's gross. And so is she. A right little Miss Nice-as-pie."

"But nice-as-pie no longer, Killer!" shouted Lois, pulling off the mask. "For with Souperman's help, I have revealed you to be a Public Enemy Number One – a Ratatouille Enemy!"

Lois turned to me. "How can I ever thank you, Souperman?"

"Don't mention it," I said.

"Too late, I already have," said Lois.

"Then it's about time you tested yourself on Enemy-Handling Techniques," I said. And so she did...

How To Handle Your Enemies: Stage Two

Test yourself on Souperman's Enemy-Handling Techniques

1: What would you give a Bangers and Mash Enemy?

   (i) Five minutes in the microwave.

   (ii) A good dollop of tomato ketchup.
   (iii) The imposter treatment.

2: Where will you find secret advice on handling a Chicken Tikka Enemy?

   (i) In an Hencyclopedia.

   (ii) In the Eggs-Files.
   (iii) In *How To Handle Your Enemies*.

3: Which of the following is the correct name for an enemy with a really big head?

    (i)   Hugh Jolly.

    (ii)   Norm Us-Great-Pizza.

    (iii) Big Whoppa.

4: Why is a Toady-in-the-Hole Enemy so called?

    (i)   Because they're always hanging about the croakrooms.

    (ii)   Because they're slippery and slimy.

    (iii) Because they're always toadying to the teacher.

5: What's another name for a Ratatouille Enemy?

    (i)   A right mug.

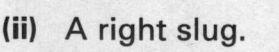

    (ii)   A right slug.

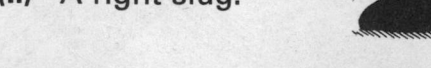

    (iii) A right thug.

ANSWERS:

1: **(i)** 0 points. WARNING!!!! Do *not* try this. You could ruin your mum's microwave.

(ii) 5 points. This is no way to handle a bangers and mash enemy, but it is really good fun!

(iii) 10 points.

2: **(i)** 0 points. Think you'll find anything useful in here? You'll be c-lucky.

(ii) 5 points. It's too scary. You'd only chicken out.

(iii) 10 points. What a brilliant brain you have!

3: **(i)** 0 points. *You're* the lolly – a melted lolly i.e. a big drip!

(ii) 5 points. You must have a brain like a pizza – very thick and crusty!

(iii) 10 points. Well done, which is just the way I like my Big Whoppers.

4: (i) 10 points.

(ii) 10 points. Well done! You're obviously an ex in this field.

(iii) 10 points. From your head to your toad.

5: (i) 0 points. *You're the mug.*

(ii) 5 points. That's a real insult! To slugs that is.

(iii) 10 points. You've hit the nail on the head! (As opposed to the Ratatouille Enemy who is likely to hit *you* on the head.)

SCORES: **0-10 points.** You'll never become Souperman. Cuppa-Souperman perhaps, but never Souperman.

10-30. You're a bit of a bird brain, so I suppose you might become a Bird's-Nest-Souperman.

30-50. Y-e-es! You really know what to *do*. In fact, you're a Souper-Do-per-man!

How To Handle Your Enemies: Stage Three

Souperman's Tup Sicrit Cudi

To create your very own Public Enemy File, you need a top secret code. And as all Public Enemies are total fools, it needs to be foolproof. Codes can be really complicated. In fact, they can be just like a bump on the head, i.e. a real pain. So here's a secret code you can do standing on your head, which, if you've forgotten to turn the book the other way up after reading *How To Handle Your Friends*, you're probably doing anyway.

Take the five vowels:

A E I O U

Now bring them back, and simply swop each vowel for another one, so:

A becomes **E**

E becomes **I**

I becomes **O**

O becomes **U**

U becomes **A**

Dead easy, eh! Or rather... Died iesy! That way Billy Bonegrinder won't ever know you're writing about him, because you'll be writing about someone called Bolly Bunigrondir! And if Billy Bonegrinder ever says to you ...

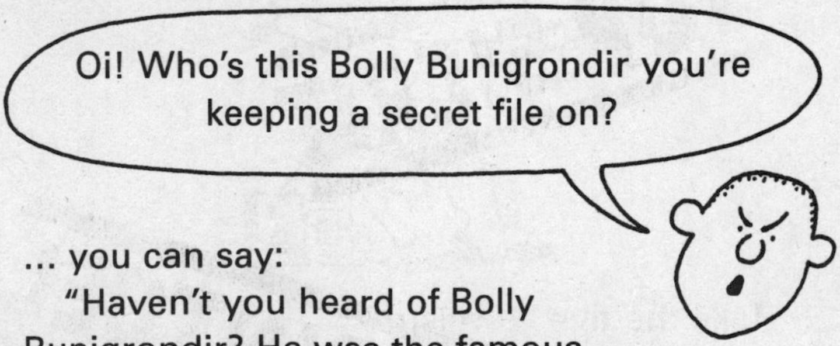

Oi! Who's this Bolly Bunigrondir you're keeping a secret file on?

... you can say:
"Haven't you heard of Bolly Bunigrondir? He was the famous Viking warrior who scared his enemies by dressing up as a giant Buni-rabbit."

Pabloc Inimy
Fole